I once kr
who wo

poems
by Emma Purshouse

pictures
by Catherine Pascall Moore

performing ideas
by Figment (of the Imagination)

Fair Acre Press

Every book has a page that describes who owns the work. This is ours:

First published 2016 by Fair Acre Press

This book has been typeset in Comic Sans

Printed and bound by CPI Group (UK) Ltd, Croydon CR0 4YY

ISBN 978-1-911048-02-2   www.fairacrepress.co.uk

Emma would like to thank

all the children who have come to workshops and performances that she has done in schools and libraries across the country over the years.

Many of the poems in this book were written as a direct response to requests from young people for poems on particular subjects.

Thank you also to the members of the Stoke-on-Trent Young Writers' Group and the Wolverhampton Home Educated Creative Writers for all of their constructive criticism and feedback on both the illustrations and the poetry.

Thanks also goes to Jocelyn Gronow for help in regard to making the book dyslexic-friendly and to Jim Sheehan, Paul Francis and Keith Chandler for their advice, support, and wise words.

And finally a huge hug for Kelsey Keeling who took the time to read every single poem and look closely at each illustration before giving the manuscript a final thumbs up from a 9 year old's viewpoint.

Acknowledgements

Some of these poems have been published in other places before they were published in this book:

What would a dinosaur dine on?, Chocolate Labrador, and
An elderly lady phones the police station to report her tortoise
missing (again) under the title Someone has stolen my tortoise
appeared in "Born to Giggle", a Save the Children poetry anthology
(2012).

Nevil the Starfish, Insomni-yak and Insomni-gnu
were shortlisted in the Belmont Children's Poetry Prize in 2005.

The Potts and their spots, and Mal de Mer were published
in The Caterpillar magazine (Winter 2013).

Nevil the Starfish, Maybe tomorrow we'll walk to school,
He's got claws too!, The Barrel, What would a dinosaur dine on?,
Spelling it out (as Eke), Anony Mouse, Gnats, Chocolate Labrador,
Insomni-yak and Insomni-gnu, The snail's shell is curious,
Someone has stolen my tortoise, The 'Princess of Halloween',
Luke Baddun's Zoo, Jeevan's Opal and the Dragon's Egg,
Patent Pending (as I've invented a contraption),
The problem with bluebottles (as Blue bottle) were all
previously available on the Fair or Fowl CD, published by
Rowan Berry Press.

We dedicate this book to

Gwenllian Bevan, Myfi Bevan, Beca Bevan-Silk,
Elliw Bevan-Silk, Aeryn Boniface, Jaxon Boniface,
Lucas Bray, Edmund Brook, Josephene Calcutt-Barker,
Oliver Calcutt, Thomas Calcutt,
Alexandre Miguel Carter da Fonseca, Seb Carter,
Jessica Chandler, Kitty Chandler, Matthew Channon,
Bella Clark, Camilla Clark, Georgia Clark, Tom Draper,
Zak Gittoes, Zalie Gittoes, Zara Gittoes, Ziva Gittoes,
Zoe Gittoes, Megan Gronow, Rebecca Gronow,
Dominic Hall, Claire Howland, Eloise Howland,
Anna-Tina Jashapara, Charlotte Kingsley,
Ellie-Rose Kingsley, Freddie Kingsley, James Kingsley,
Sam Kingsley, Poppy 'Dandelion' Lovell,
Rochea Lovell-Forbes, Jack Maggs, William Maggs,
Lily Mallin, Lola Mallin, Archie Moir, Watson Moir,
William Pascall Moore, Annie Pengelly, Jessie Pengelly,
Alma Pernas Freeth, Santi Pernas Freeth, Olive Playle,
The Potts Family (and their spots),
Olive Seabourne-Elliot, Alice Sheehan, Ella Sheehan,
Elsie Skan, Sid Skan, Abbie Steward,
Joseph Steward, Jack Stockton, Thea Swinscoe,
Oscar Welch, Stanley Welch, Robin Whitmarsh,
Dhilan Williams, Shay Williams,
Clara Yapp, Georgia Yapp, Solomon Yapp, Tommy Yapp,

and YOU!

How do I learn a poem?

First of all find a poem. There are lots of books in your local library to choose from. Some story books for very little children rhyme, so if you have younger brothers or sisters take a look at the sort of books they read. They might have some good poems amongst them. Do make sure you pick a poem that you really, really like.

Choose a poem with rhymes and a strong rhythm. This should help you remember it. You can learn free verse, but it's a bit harder to do. Don't let me put you off if you are feeling brave. Learn the poem a small chunk at a time. Focus on the first two lines or the first four lines to begin with.

I walk about to learn my poems. The rhythm of walking seems to help. I say the lines out loud, over and over and over. Perhaps you could do the same thing on your way to and from school. When you have got the first chunk learnt, do the next chunk in the same way.

You will need to carry a copy of the poem with you to help you when you are first learning it. When you think the whole of the poem is learnt, still keep practising. Run it through a couple of times a day. Tell it to the dog or cat, the mirror, your great aunty Ethel.

Always do it out loud. This will make sure that the poem gets from your short term memory into your long term memory. I sometimes practise in the bath! Or sometimes I say my poem a couple of times before I go to sleep.

You might find that there are certain bits of the poem that you always forget. That happens sometimes. What I do is - I think of a hand movement or a facial expression that I can use with the word or the line that I've been forgetting.

I do the movement every time I say the line. This seems to help me remember my words. It's a bit weird but it works for me.

When you truly believe your poem is learned, start to perform it...

Use your face and your body to express things. You don't need to do this for every part of the poem, but certain things might need emphasis. For example, if somebody is said to be waving in a poem then why don't you wave? If there is something surprising in a poem, then you might make your face show shock.

Maybe the whole poem is in the voice of a character? If so work out how the character might speak. Some poems might be partly narrated and then have a character speaking a couple of lines, so have one voice for the narrator and one for the character.

Why not have a go at performing to an audience? Invite family to listen. Could you share a poem with your school friends? Remember, if you do forget your poem in front of the audience it isn't the end of the world.

It's just a poem. The sun will still come up, your friends and family will still love you. I have forgotten poems sometimes. If I do I just say, 'Sorry, I've forgotten my poem,' to the audience, and then I laugh about it before leaving the stage.

There are lots of poems in this book that you could learn and perform. Look out for Figment (of the Imagination).

Figment is an ideas flea, and he will be flitting amongst the pages to give you some top tips about how to learn and perform some of the different poems here. And most importantly don't forget to have fun!

Best wishes
Emma P
xxx

Contents

Psst, I'm Figment (of the Imagination) - pleased to meet you, here's my card

Flights of fancy are my speciality.
I can organise a trip,
take your wits on a kind of daydream
or your brain on a moonlight flit.
Hurry it up. Book now. Be ready
to let reality sort of slip.
Phase out, chillax, glaze over,
make stuff up, believe in it.

Ready, steady, set your mind free,
let it go, watch it run.
Bear hunting on the moon?
Yeah. As soon as it's said it's done.
You can swim with orange dolphins
on the far side of the sun.
Why not sprout some swan wings?
Let your thoughts fly. Have some fun!

Psst... I'm Figment, do you like reading aloud? Why not imagine my voice as I whisper in your ear to encourage day dreaming? Have a go at reading this poem using a voice like mine.

Poems I have known

Poems can be thin.
Poems can be fat.
I once knew a poem
who wore a hat.
Poems can be mad,
bad, crazy and weird.
Most are clean shaven,
though this has a beard!
Poems talk nonsense
and onomatopoeia.
Poems can calm you
or fill you with fear.
Poems have rhythm.
Poems have rhyme.
My uncle was a poem
who turned to crime.
Poems can be gentle.
Poems can be kind.
Poems can be fact
or a figment of the mind.
There are poems you'll love
and poems you'll hate.
There are poems to be shared
with your mum or your mate.
There are poems for the page
and poems for the stage.
There are poems in this book,

so come and have a look.
Make friends with a poem.
Read one today.
Then should anyone ask
you can shout up and say,
"Poems are wicked.
Poems are nice.
And some of them it seems
have been written by mice!"

Spelling it out

"Eke!"
squeaked the mouse
as she taught her children
a valuable lesson
in saving cheese
for later.

Anony Mouse

Anony Mouse is quite prolific
when it comes to writing verse,
but sadly for Anony
no one ever knows it's hers.

By Anony Mouse

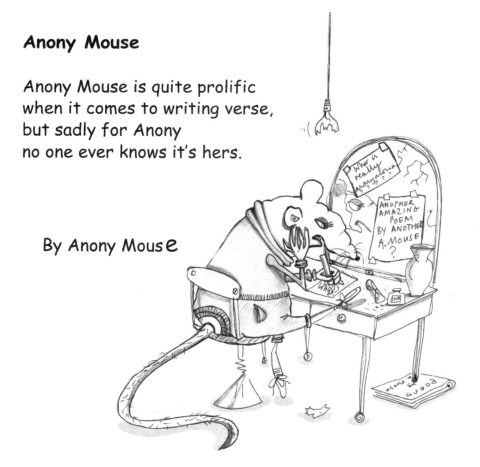

The snail's shell is curious

The snail's shell is curious.
  It doesn't seem to fit the snail.
    He'd be better in a banana skin -
      he could stretch out his slimy tail.

        Although I can foresee a problem
          when you peel back the skin
            of your yummy, yellow banana
            and you find a snail within.

Missing – one iguana, partial to cheese

I've lost my iguana.
I've lost her in the park.
Can someone help me find her?
She doesn't like the dark.

    I've lost my iguana,
    perhaps she's up that tree.
    Can someone help me coax her down
    with half a pound of Brie?

I've lost my iguana,
is that her over there?
"Come on Iggy, darling,
I've got some Camembert."

    I've lost my iguana.
    The evening's getting colder.
    "I'll take you to the deli;
    we can buy some Gorgonzola."

I've lost my iguana,
I've tried Edam, Quark and Swiss,
yelled Cheddar and Caerphilly.
I wonder where she is?

I've lost my iguana,
will nothing bring her back?
Neither Feta nor Halloumi
or a slice of Pepper Jack?

I've lost my iguana.
I'm running out of cheeses.
I hope that I can find her
before the weather freezes.

I've lost my iguana,
I don't know what to do.
I'm stood here like a daft thing
shouting, "Danish Blue!"

Here comes my iguana,
I really thought I'd lost her,
until I tried the magic words,
"Hoorah, for Double Gloucester!"

Crumbs

I wrote a poem
on a biscuit
which was quite absurd.

I read it back,
edited, and then
I ate my words!

Want to learn a poem?
Keep repeating a bite sized chunk
at a time until you know it without
looking at the words. Then move on
to the next bit.

Feeling Sheepish

I have sheep
shaped slippers,
two of them,
a pair.
I wear them
on my feet
but now Spring is in the air
the left one has started baaing,
the right one sometimes skips,
and they've been nibbling
at the carpet
just a little bit.

Chocolate Labrador

We were going to get a pet,
a chocolate Labrador.
Mum said it would be great
but me, I wasn't sure.

She could see that I was worried.
I told her how I felt,
that I'd rather have a real dog
because a chocolate one might melt!

He's got claws too!

I've been bitten
by our kitten
and I really don't know why

All I did was:-

> tickle his tummy
> tug his tail
> wiggle his whiskers
> pinch his nose
> and
> dress him up all nice
> in my little sister's
> clothes

I've been bitten
by our kitten
and I really don't know why

I've been bitten
by our kitten
and I think I'm going to cry

WAAAAHHHHHHHHHHHHHHHHHHHHHHH!

What would a dinosaur dine on?

What would a dinosaur dine on
if he came to our house for tea?

Would
burgers and chips
and ice cream and jelly
and Kentucky Fried Chicken
fill up his belly?

Or
would he
raid our fridge
and our freezer?
Our cupboards?
Our larder?
Would he clean-out
the greenhouse
and gobble
the garden?

And
if he still wasn't
full after that,
would he
munch on
the goldfish?
The gerbils?
The cat?

Would he
chomp on
my sister
or my older brother?

Would he
chew up
my father,
crunch up
my mother?

And then

oh my life
what if he...

wanted a pudding

and the pudding

was me?

Mal de Mer

The sea was heaving,
he threw up
a starfish
and a bivalve mollusc
(it was the clam before the storm).

He began
roiling and boiling
and thrashing and crashing
and bashing the rocks
and lashing the shore.
He awoke the kittiwakes
and scared all the buoys and gulls.

Sick of himself,
sick of making waves,
he went out
and took some deep breaths.

When he came back in
he was feeling fine,
quite well,
just swell.

The Potts and their spots

William Potts
seldom got spots
because he ate his greens.

Jonathan Potts
had one or two spots
but that was normal for teens.

Ellen Potts
never got spots
her complexion was truly supreme.

Mom and Dad Potts
had billions of spots,
dining solely on chocolate ice cream.

If I was a spider
I would not get wider
Eating flies for my dinner
I would surely get thinner

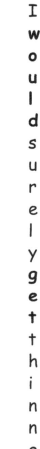
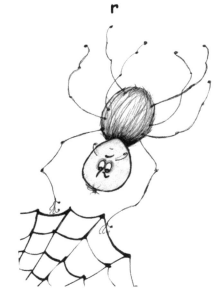
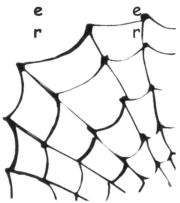

The problem with bluebottles

When I saw the bluebottle
buzzing in my hall
I was most put out to see it.
I wasn't pleased at all.

I tried my best to catch it
with some ladders and a net
but it flew up in the corner
and I haven't caught it yet.

Buzzzzzzzzzzzzzzzzzzzzzzz

Psst This one is fun to perform if you make a buzzing noise after some of the lines of the poem and pretend you are looking up in the air for the bluebottle.

Too much of a good thing

Oh man, oh man, oh man!
Miss Chamberlain loves her marzipan.

She eats it morning,
noon and night,
says,"It's so much tastier
than Turkish Delight."

Oh man, oh man, oh man!
Miss Chamberlain loves her marzipan.

She eats it for breakfast,
for dinner, for tea.
"It's scrummy," she shouts.
"And it's all for me!"

Oh man, oh man, oh man!
Miss Chamberlain loves her marzipan.

She has some in her desk
and some in her car
and some in the staff room
that she hides in a jar.

Oh man, oh man, oh man!
Miss Chamberlain loves her marzipan.

At break she ate a piece
that was one metre thick
and five minutes later
boy, was she sick!

Oh man, oh man, oh man!
Miss Chamberlain's gone off marzipan.

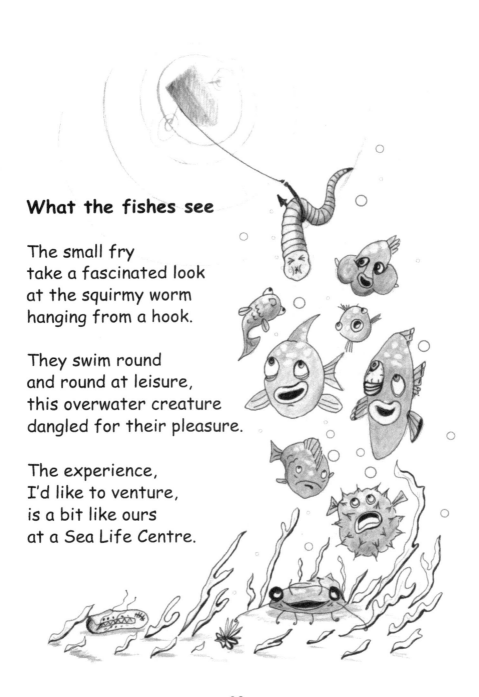

What the fishes see

The small fry
take a fascinated look
at the squirmy worm
hanging from a hook.

They swim round
and round at leisure,
this overwater creature
dangled for their pleasure.

The experience,
I'd like to venture,
is a bit like ours
at a Sea Life Centre.

Whodunnit, duck?

Oh upside down duck
on your feathery back you float.
Were you run over by a boat?

Your head forever dabbling,
suspended in midstream.
Was it a vicious strain of bream?

Your orange-webbed feet
turned up to the sun.
Was it the farmer with his gun?

Knit one, purl one, ribbit!

My grandma has a hobby,
she knits cardigans for frogs.
She worries about them catching colds
in muddy pools and bogs.

She chooses wool in shades of green
(with an eye on camouflage).
Her cardies outwit herons
and she doesn't even charge.

This year she's gone for something new,
(never does things by halves).
She's bought a lorry load of brown wool,
now she's knitting tadpole scarves.

An elderly lady phones the police station to report her tortoise missing (again).

Someone has stolen my tortoise.
It really isn't right.
Someone has stolen my tortoise.
They took it away in the night.

Someone has stolen my tortoise.
He was five years younger than me.
Someone has stolen my tortoise.
He was only eighty three.

Someone has stolen my tortoise.
I'm worried they've nicked him to sell.
Someone has stolen my tortoise.
I'm going through tortoise hell.

Someone has stolen my tortoise.
They did exactly the same last year.
Someone has stolen my tortoise.
It's a shock when they disappear.

These poems work for two performers. If you are a good actor, you can perform them on your own. You will need your best old lady voice and a police officer voice.

A police officer responds to the elderly lady who reported her tortoise missing (again).

No one has stolen your tortoise.
This happens every November.
No one has stolen your tortoise.
I've explained it before. Do you remember?

No one has stolen your tortoise.
And there's no need to come down the station.
No one has stolen your tortoise.
You're a victim of hibernation.

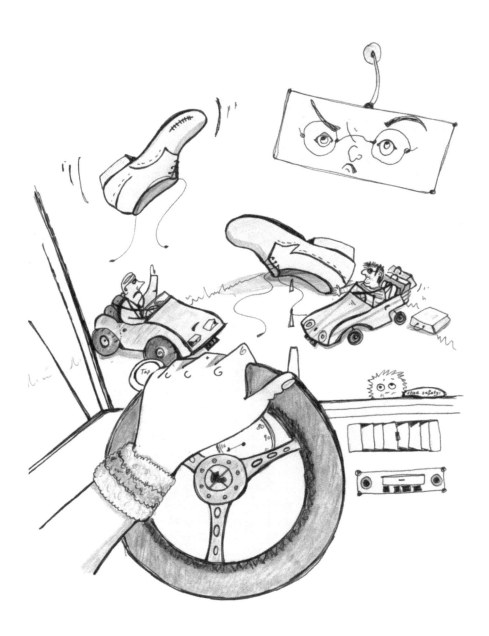

Giant Shoe Clearance

Giants shouldn't kick off shoes
and leave them willy-nilly.
It causes havoc with the traffic,
this behaviour is quite silly.

They cleared the giant's shoes.
They used a winch and crane,
and issued him a ticket
so he won't do it again.

The Barrel

When the postman came calling
he gave me a shock,
"Good morning, hello,
wakey-wakey, knock-knock.
I'm delivering your barrel
so please can you sign
just by this cross
on the dotted line."

I took hold of his pen
and I did as he said,
as all kinds of thoughts
zipped and zoomed through my head.
"Who in the world
would send me a present?
What a surprise! Oh, so thoughtful!
How terribly pleasant!"

But the barrel was big
and the barrel was wide
and it took me an hour
to get it inside.
I pushed and I pulled,
I was panting and shaking
and a little perturbed
by the noise it was making.

Yes, the barrel was whispering,
chattering and chirping,
and I'm sure that I heard
some cackling and burping.
There was only one thing to do
so I fled
straight down the garden
and into my shed.

I grabbed a crowbar!
Then do you know what I did?
I went back to that barrel
and I prised off the lid.
Ahhhh! A monkey explosion!
They shot out like rockets.
My eyeballs very nearly popped
out of their sockets!

47

I started to count
and I'd got up to seven
before I spotted four more
and then that made eleven.
Oh, my goodness! My word!
There's one in the oven.
Did I say eleven?
Better make that a dozen!

They were climbing the curtains
and hanging from doors,
they were skating around
on the laminate floors.
They were eating the fruit
from out of my bowl,
they were running amok,
I was losing control.

I panicked, I freaked,
I made myself scarce,
I hid in the cupboard
under the stairs.
I listened to the sounds
of mayhem and riot.
Until, finally, at night fall
everything became quiet.

When I came out of hiding,
I searched high and low,
on the lookout for monkeys.
Where did they all go?
My home seemed deserted.
I thought they'd all fled,
till I found the whole troop
fast asleep in my bed!

I tangled their tails,
and I tied a big knot,
picked them up like bananas,
in a bunch, the whole lot!
They were struggling and fighting
and making a din,
but I dragged them back to that barrel
and I bundled them in.

I jammed on the lid
with one bang and three thwacks,
before hammering it shut
with some nails and some tacks.
I rolled that big barrel
out into my yard,
then sat up all night
to think long and think hard.

About off-loading monkeys
I had no idea,
all that I knew was
they weren't stopping here.
I was completely confused
about what I should do,
so I've stuck on ten stamps
and I've sent them to you!

Learn this one if you dare!
Difficult but not impossible. Act it
out to help you remember it.
Keep practising.

The Hat

This poem wears a floppy hat.
It covers up its face.
It can't see where it's going
which is why it's often late.

The hat is sunflower yellow
with a bright red spotted bow,
but what on earth is under it
is hard for me to know.

When the attention span
is smaller than the wing span...

Flitter, flutter, flitter, fly.
I can't remember. Who am I?

Drizzled kipper?
Sizzled dipper?
Twizzled tripper?
Mizzled quipper?
Frizzled flipper?
Chiselled slipper!

Oh dear, that can't be right!
Fuzzy face, spots of white,
antennae things,
earth brown wings.

I'm a GRIZZLED SKIPPER! Yes! Yipee!
A grizzled skipper: that's definitely ME!

Flitter, flutter, flitter, fly.
Doh! It's gone again. Who am I?

Gnats

What's the point of a gnat?
I gnow gnot what they do.
Although I gnow they have big gnashers -
that one's just bitten you!

A whole bunch of trouble

Last Tuesday I squished a banana
underfoot with a stamp of my boot.
The RSPCB
have arrested me
and charged me with cruelty to fruit.

Nevil the Starfish

Nevil the starfish
was sick of his shape,
so he made a wish
(upon himself)
that he could be
something else
like a squarefish
or a roundfish
or a hexagonal, octagonal, nonagonagal fish.
Even a triangle fish
would have done.
But when you wish
upon a star
fish,
it doesn't matter who you are,
your dreams they don't come true.

Ask a friend to help you as you read this poem out. Get them to draw the shapes in the air as you say them. Watch them find it more and more difficult.

Bird Watching on the Cornish Coast

I saw a black-backed gull
in Tintagel,
a pair of peregrines
near Padstow,
three puffins just off
Perranporth
and pigeons
in Polperro.

But the birds
I'd really gone to see
remained elusive
and tourist information
were no help.
The woman behind the counter
looked askance
as I enquired
about
the parrots
of
Penzance!

here to
help!

gulls ✓
peregrines ✓
puffins ✓
pigeons ✓
parrots ✗

Psst have you spotted it?
The first verse of the poem opposite is an alliterative tongue twister! Try saying it as fast as you can.

Water's Holiday

Water went on holiday
to visit cousin Fire.
Perhaps he should have phoned
as it's politer to enquire

if folk would like a visit
and you shouldn't just assume
that family want your company
or even have the room.

When Water came a-sloshing,
he knocked at Fire's place,
he gargled through the letter box
then pressed his drippy face

up at Fire's window,
"Fire, Fire. Are you in?
I really swish you'd answer,"
babbled Water. What a din!

He bubbled, glugged and gurgled,
feeling sure that Fire was near,
but for all his splishy-sploshing
Water couldn't make him hear.

Fire smouldered in the garden
as his dogs all started barking.
He came crackling up the path,
hot, bothered and remarking,

"What the blazes! Who might that be?
Not expecting anyone!"
He took his time to answer
(half hoping that they'd gone).

When he saw his cousin Water
with carriers in hand,
Fire started seething
as he really hadn't planned

for a visit in the summertime
from such a wet relation.
Poor Fire's heart began to sink.
It filled with trepidation.

"Slurprise! It's me," gushed Water.
Fire gave a little hiss,
as Water leapt upon him,
and swamped him with a kiss.

"Oh, sorry to arrive on spec,"
sniffed Water with a pout.
"I can see by your expression
I've completely put you out."

Find a voice for Water and one for
Fire. How would these elements speak
if they could?

See, mums do know everything

"Mum,
how would you ring a ring-tailed lemur?"
I wasn't sure; I had to ask her.

"Son,
you'd have to save your money up
and find the code for Madagascar."

It might be catching

I'm shivering. I'm shaking.
My body's all aching.

I'm hot then I'm cold.
I feel a million years old.

Arrrrr! Look at my tongue.
My legs are on wrong.

The fronts are the backs.
I've the knees of a yak.

I think it's the flu.
I might give it to you...

A A A Choooooooooooooooooooo

Frog March

Frog, frog, frog, frog,
frog, frog, frog, frog,
frog, frog, frog, frog,
frog, frog, frog, frog.

About turn!

Frog, frog, frog, frog,
frog, frog, frog, frog,
frog, frog, frog, frog,
frog, frog, frog, frog.

Squad halt! Stand at ease!

Right, you 'orrible little lot, now hop it!

Shout or sing the chorus between each verse. If you've got an audience watching, why not get them to shout the chorus with you? How do you think Mud might talk?

My Name is Mud

*I live in the high-rise mud flats
on the wrong side of the city.
I make all kinds of slurps and splats.
I'm dirty, mean and sticky.*

I steal cars and race about,
slinging sludge as I pass by.
To pedestrians I shout,
"Here's mud in your eye!"

*I live in the high-rise mud flats
on the wrong side of the city.
I make all kinds of slurps and splats.
I'm dirty, mean and sticky.*

They've put up a warning sign;
I'm in the highway code.
Quick, dial 999.
Danger, mud is on the road!

> *I live in the high-rise mud flats*
> *on the wrong side of the city.*
> *I make all kinds of slurps and splats.*
> *I'm dirty, mean and sticky.*

I'm a slippy, slidey driver.
I don't obey the rules.
(I ain't got a licence either).
I think the cops are fools.

> *I live in the high-rise mud flats*
> *on the wrong side of the city.*
> *I make all kinds of slurps and splats.*
> *I'm dirty, mean and sticky.*

The law try hard to catch me.
They try for all they're worth,
but they don't stand a chance see
'cos I'm quick to go to earth.

> *I live in the high-rise mud flats*
> *on the wrong side of the city.*
> *I make all kinds of slurps and splats.*
> *I'm dirty, mean and sticky.*

I'm a creature with many faces
and when I'm running from the feds
I've got a million hiding places.
Shhh! I'm in your trainer treads!

I live in the high-rise mud flats
on the wrong side of the city.
I make all kinds of slurps and splats.
I'm dirty, mean and sticky.

My dragon, Spike
for Freda

Spike my dragon is very chatty.
He talks and talks nonstop.
(Although most of it is dragon speak
which can be a bit smoky and hot).

He yawps and scrawps and yodels.
He junters and jaloppies.
I feed him mainly on carrots
but he's partial to soft mints and poppies.

He'd like someone to play with,
someone other than me,
so if you've got a dragon friend
please bring him round to tea.

The Best in Pest Control

Have you heard slithering noises at night?
Have you seen glittering eyes reflect light
from the darkest corners of your room?
Have your firelighters been nibbled when you're
not looking?
Have you smelt smoke when nothing is cooking?

Are you being TROUBLED BY DRAGONS?
Call George the Dragon Slayer.

No dragon too big or too small.
No dragon too tiny or tall.
All dragons brought to their knees.
Satisfaction Guaranteed.

Cross George's palm with gold
and consider the problem solved!

* State of the art dragon traps!
** Cut price zombie, demon and werewolf service
available throughout October.

Lost Glove

On the spike of the fence
is a lifeless, black mitten.
Others might see useless glove
but me I'm seeing a kitten.
Pipe cleaners for his whiskers,
green buttons for his eyes,
felt triangles for ears.
Now put your hand inside.
Bend and flex your fingers,
make your kitten nod and bow,
learn to throw your voice,
make him purr, meow.
With a wiggle of your thumb,
voilà, we're talking muppet.
With a little imagination,
a lost glove becomes a puppet.

The capture of Mud
is recounted for the court

Your Honour, he left his prints
on the pristine kitchen floor.
We followed the dirty devil's trail
through from the back door.

We tracked him down the hall,
then onwards up the stairs,
"We're closing in now mud boy,
it's time to say your prayers."

> *His name is Mud*
> *He's bad not good*
> *Give him seven years m'lud*

It wasn't hard to find him,
their carpets were all white,
their taste was modern, minimal
and the accused is none too bright.

We trailed him to a bedroom,
where we found the little brute
who was hiding in exhibit A,
this grubby walking boot.

> *His name is Mud*
> *He's bad not good*
> *Give him seven years m'lud*

We put the cuffs on tight,
he's a slippery little creature,
then took him down the cells,
banged him up. "Now, that'll teach ya!"

Send him down your honour
for a long stretch in the nick.
He needs to know crime doesn't pay.
It's time to make mud stick.

His name is Mud
He's bad not good
Give him seven years m'lud

Cat-egorically Speaking

I don't want
a howling cat
I don't want
a yowling cat
I don't want
a fat cat
or a thin cat
I don't want
a good cat
or a bad cat
I don't want
a cat in a hat
or even
a cat in a coat
I don't want
a cat that goes
for the throat
I don't want
a white cat
or a black cat
I don't want
a cat
er pillar
or a cat
as trophe

I don't want
a cat that looks
like me

72

I don't want
a tall cat
or a small cat
I definitely
don't want
a bald cat
I WANT
A BIG CAT!
THE BIGGEST
CAT I EVER
SAW!
I WANT
A LION!
ROAR!

This poem wrote itself with a Liverpudlian accent. Go on have a go at doing one! Did it work? Try it in another accent. Glaswegian? Black Country?

Dear Big Ears

Our grandad's got the biggest ears.
He's been growing them for years.

They're large-lobed and full of hair.
They're so big that people stop. And stare.

Though taunts and teases fill the air,
our big-eared grandad doesn't care,

he never hears a word, not one,
his hearing has completely gone!

So we've decided that we'd better
let him know our thoughts (by letter).

Dear Grandad,

Please understand,
that things are getting out
of hand.
Your giant ears are now an
issue;
We can't get close enough
to kiss you.
We want you here with us
forever
    and wouldn't want to
change you.
        Never!
But could you get those lug
holes pinned?
We'd hate to lose you in
the wind.
        xxx

Thoughts on teeth

Toothpaste.
Use it a lot
so your teeth don't rot.
Brush three times a day
the dentists say
to avoid a filling,
dreadful drilling,
and killing
people
with your breath.

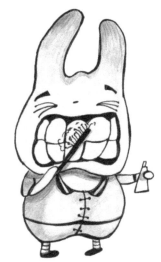

Cousin Keith
has clean teeth

Gertie doesn't brush
her teeth are dirty

Uncle Moss
makes time
to floss

Louise
has gum disease

Jack
has
plaque
yak

Charlie Mingalitis
has a nasty case
of gingivitis

And the Queen.....................

she has a crown!

This could work with as many as thirteen voices. Make a soundproof hat for voice three to wear. What would it look like? In verse four each person could say their own noise word.

Miss Onomatopoeia conducts the school band

Voice 1	Miss Onomatopoeia waves her baton.
Voice 2	(Miss Onomatopoeia has a soundproof hat on).
Voice 3	"Girls and boys let's make some noise!"
Voice 4	ring a ring ring
Voice 5	screech screech screech
Voice 6	ting a ting ting
Voice 7	boom boom boom
Voice 8	ching a ching ching
Voice 9	crash crash crash
Voice 10	bang a bang bang
Voice 11	bash bash bash
Voice 12	hoot toot hoot
Voice 13	clash clash clash

All Voices	ring a ring screech ting
	boom a boom toot ching
	bang a bang bash
	hoot clash CRASH!

Voice 1	Miss Onomatopoeia
	waves her baton.
Voice 2	(Miss Onomatopoeia
	has a soundproof hat on).
Voice 3	"Girls and boys
	we've made some noise!"

Luke Baddun's Zoo

Mrs Baddun, we want our money back!
Luke charged us 50p!
He promised to show wild animals
to Tyrone, Chantelle and me.

He said that he'd got big cats!
He's a rotten little liar!
We saw a single tubby tabby:
it was snoozing by the fire.

The giant tortoise from Galapagos
turned out to be a wok,
while the world's longest python
had googly eyes - it was a sock!

Goldie the killer whale, hah!
That speaks for itself.
How could anyone fit an orca
into a bowl on the kitchen shelf?

And the sleepy newborn bear cub
was the biggest con trick ever.
It was the mouldy, fake fur, hat
that his gran wears in cold weather.

As for the invisible rabbit,
we couldn't contain our rage.
There was simply nothing there
except a carrot in a cage.

What's that? Luke's not in?
He's gone to get the bus?
He's going to a real zoo
with the money he took from us?

And you won't be giving refunds,
zero, nothing, nil?
You think Luke has imagination
and entrepreneurial skill?

Well, we're glad you can see the funny side
because the hippopotamus was a laugh -
Luke let us peep through the keyhole
at **you**! You were in the bath!

Christmas Tree Snakes

Did I see that tinsel
slither round the tree?
Can anyone hear that hissing
or is it only me?

Was that bauble blinking
as it swirled and caught the light?
Or was it a reptilian eye
shining clear and bright?

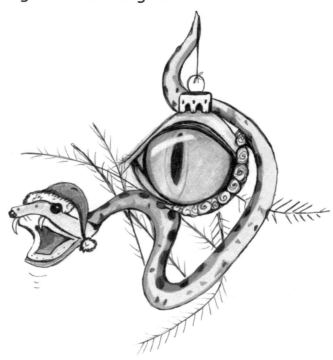

You don't need three people to read this aloud. You could just change your own voice and play all the characters yourself.

Jonah and the Wail

Voice 1 - narrator

Jonah wailed
inside the whale
inside the whale
he wailed.

Voice 2 - whale

Hey, landlubber,
why d'ya blubber?
You'll never make a sailor.

Voice 3 - Jonah

The damp has made
my asthma worse
and I've forgotten my inhaler!

Voice 1 - narrator

Jonah wailed
inside the whale
inside the whale
he wailed.

Voice 2 - whale

Yeah

All Voices

Jonah wailed
inside the whale
inside the whale
he wailed.

The 'Princess of Halloween'

The 'Princess of Halloween'
was under worked,
if you know what I mean.
For girls in tiaras
and pink frilly frocks,
at this time of year...
Work?
Not a lot!

As her agent rightly said,
"There's more of a call
for the living dead
or for those sort of people
who are minus a head!
There's a market
for things that go bump
in the night
and acts that can give folk
a bit of a fright,
warlocks, spirits,
ghosties and ghouls.
It's the 31st of October
I'm afraid there are rules!
You're blonde and blue-eyed
and terribly pretty,
but your look's ten a penny
they want something more
witchy!

Now,
if you could grow
a mole
or a wart
or even a spot..."

"What!"
screeched the Princess,
"Certainly not!
I'm talented,
I'm beautiful,
I'm gorgeous,
I'm hot!"

"Hmmm,"
said her agent.
"It's Halloween
and you're not!"

The Princess was shocked.

She stamped her feet.
She started to cry.
She gave her agent
the evil eye!
But if you think she gave up
well you're sadly mistaken,
instead she went in for a
transformation.

For once she'd got over
her tantrums and sobbing,
the Princess perfected
her apple bobbing;
worked very hard
on her tricking and treating,
developed her spelling
and then phoned
for a meeting
with an image consultant
who said,
"Try painting the palace
with matt black emulsion
and doing away
with your lifelong compulsion
to buy lots of glittery things
like diaphanous dresses
and fairy wings."
So the Princess bought hair dye
called 'Raven Wing Black,'
some long stripy socks
and a tall pointy hat,
and believe it or not
a sleek slinky cat.
She practised a cackle
that could make windows rattle.
She adopted an air
of perpetual gloom,
then to finish it off
she borrowed a broom.

The Princess went back to her agent
who whistled
and said,
"That's excellent
your highness.
The **hex** factor.
You've got it!
I can certainly find you some work
now you're Gothic!"

Maybe tomorrow we'll walk to school

Beep-beep.
Toot-toot.
Traffic!
Oh, terrific!

Beep-beep.
Toot-toot.
Traffic!
It's horrific.

Beep-beep.
Toot-toot.
Feeling manic,
in a panic,
travel sick!

Beep-beep.
Toot-toot.
Should've brought
a picnic,
a banana
and a biscuit.

Beep-beep.
Toot-toot.
Wish that I
was still in bed!
Rev, rev, rev.
Don't wanna be
a petrol head!

Beeeeeeeeeeeeeeeeeeeeeeeeeeeeeeeeeeeeeeeeeep!

Grey Cloud

Grey Cloud is here until Tuesday,
that's what the weatherman said,
but he's been here a week already
and he's starting to mess with my head.

A Native American Indian
should be fun to have round the place,
but Grey Cloud sits there sulking,
with a glum look on his face.

A course of anti-cyclonics
have done little to change his mood.
Grey Cloud is outstaying his welcome
which frankly I find rather rude.

I've put on my war paint this morning.
I've come into the garden to dance
and invoke a change in the weather.
I can't leave his departure to chance.

I'll whoop up a storm or some sunshine.
I've been waiting too long for a lull.
Anything is better than Grey Cloud,
though it pains me to say it, he's dull!

Patent Pending

I've invented a contraption
for recycling belly button fluff.
It picks it out with tweezers
as you're lounging in the buff.

It's a precision tool, its aim is true,
it hardly ever misses,
and when its collection bag is full,
(amidst blue sparks and fizzes),

click-clack will go its needles
as it starts to knit a sweater,
so at Christmas, when you find
you've no idea what to get her,

wrap the jumper up in paper
and tie it round with string,
then send it to your granny,
say, "It's just the latest thing."

My machine's a wonderful invention.
Although, there is a little glitch,
something I should mention,
just a teeny tiny hitch.

After two full years of waiting
it has come as quite a shock
to find... despite regular fluff collection
there's not enough to knit a sock!

Insomni-yak and Insomni-gnu

The Insomni-yak is rare
and the Insomni-gnu is rarer.
They'll keep you awake all night
but they don't mean to scare you.

The Insomni-yak bellows, "Wake-up."
The Insomni-gnu shouts, "Boo!"
They'll yell inside your bedclothes
and under your pillows too.

The Insomni-yak toots a trumpet.
The Insomni-gnu bangs a drum.
They'll play them in the wardrobe
to wake you, just for fun.

The Insomni-yak rides a motorbike.
The Insomni-gnu drives a bus.
They'll zoom around your ceiling
and make a humungous fuss.

The Insomni-yak owns a power drill.
The Insomni-gnu has a saw.
They'll fix what doesn't need fixing
till you just can't take any more.

The Insomni-yak lets off bangers.
The Insomni-gnu's got a rocket.
They'll make you jump in the middle of the night.
You'll wake up screaming, "Stop it!"

But there's no need to worry
because they'll be gone quite soon.
The Insomni-yak sleeps at daybreak
and the Insomni-gnu at noon.

The Insomni-yak is rare
and the Insomni-gnu is rarer.
If they kept you awake last night
they didn't mean to scare you.

Jeevan's Opal and the Dragon's Egg

"Bring back my birthstone!" Jeevan shouts.
Should he go on? He's having doubts.
"My opal was the biggest and best in the kingdom.
It brought me purity, hope and wisdom!"

In truth, he isn't feeling quite so bold.
The cave in front looks dank and cold.
But if he wants to reach the dragon's lair
he must go deeper. Will he dare?

He tries so hard to stop himself shaking
but both of his knees insist upon quaking
and when Jeevan put his hand to his sword
in the bowels of the earth something roared!

"I'm not scared of you. You lowlife! You thief!
I don't care if you **have** got razor sharp teeth.
If I must fight to the death, well that's just fine.
I've come to take back what's rightfully mine."

As Jeevan ventures into the ground
there are water drips and an echoey sound.
There's a strange shrieking – it could be rats!
There's a high-pitched squeaking – it might be bats!

Was that a voice? Or an evil laugh?
The flickering torches light his path
and all around are leaping shadows
that seem to follow as the tunnel narrows.

The walls shake. There's a violent rumbling
and the pitter pat of small stones tumbling.
Oh no! A rolling rock fills the tunnel space.
Quick, Jeevan, run! Find a passing place!

He presses himself in a handy gap.
He's cool under pressure and doesn't flap.
He's grazed by the boulder as it goes by
but Jeevan is brave and doesn't cry.

He steadies himself and takes a deep breath.
It's very hard work coming this close to death!
He's tired and hungry, he needs to rest,
but onwards and downwards - he's a lad on a quest.

What now? A really wide river of fire!
He's going to jump it. Jeevan, jump higher!
How did our hero survive such a leap?
A lesser boy would collapse in a heap.

Eek! A thousand daggers shoot out of the wall
but Jeevan is nimble and dodges them all.
Uh-oh! It seems it's not over yet.
Jeevan, look above you! Beware of that net!

That was a near miss. Cor blimey! Strewth!
Now, a million arrows rain down from the roof.
Ahhh! There's a great big hole in the floor.
Jeevan, watch out for that gaping trap door!

Whoosh! A helter-skelter with polished rock sides.
Jeevan slips in and downward he slides.
And just as it seems that the ride will not stop
he shoots out of a hole, in the wall, with a pop.

He lands in a cavern of monstrous size.
Our hero cannot believe his eyes.
There is his opal – moonlike and pale,
and wrapped around it, the dragon's tail!

Jeevan swipes with his sword: thwick, thwack.
The dragon's jaws go snickerty-snack.
They scuffle and battle, they scrap and they fight,
hour after hour, all through the night.

When the dragon shoots a fireball into the air
the backdraft singes Jeevan's hair.
But the dragon hasn't a moment to gloat
before Jeevan gets mad and goes for his throat...

He holds his blade to the dragon's chin.
"Face it scaly – it's over - I win!"
Now the dragon is crying and starts to beg,
"Kill me if you must but don't hurt my egg."

"Egg?" says Jeevan, with a puzzled look. "Where?"
The dragon points with his claw and says, "There!"
Jeevan becomes aware of a tapping.
"Told you!" says the dragon. "Look! Now it's hatching!"

On that, Jeevan's opal cracks into half,
and there on the floor sits a dragon calf.
"Ahh, bless him!" says Jeevan. "Coochie Coo."
Well, what on earth did you expect him to do?

Don't you see? Jeevan in Hindu means 'life',
So he must give up on the sword and the knife.
"No more fighting!" he says. "I think that I'd rather
take on the role of this baby's godfather."

And Jeevan swears from this moment on
his path will be an ecological one.
He will set up a dragon park, a reservation,
and do his bit for their conservation.

When you're all grown up

When you're all grown up
you can't start skipping in the street,
put your shoes on the wrong feet.
You can't hide in people's hedges
or colour over edges,
and they won't let you shoot
imaginary webs.

When you're all grown up
you can't bob your tongue or cross your eyes,
make sand castles or mud pies.
You can't kick through autumn leaves
or wipe your nose upon your sleeves,
and they won't let you ride
your bike no-handed.

When you're all grown up
you can't throw a tantrum when you're shopping,
do cartwheels or non-stop hopping.
You can't pick scabs from off your knees
or climb the lamp posts or the trees,
and they won't let you make
slurping noises through a straw.

When you're all grown up
you can't go swimming with a rubber ring,
play on a slide or have a swing.
You can't blow bubbles or dandelion clocks
or make cool stuff out of building blocks,
and they won't let you read
under your duvet with a torch.

When you're all grown up
you can't have spitting competitions,
tease pets, not even kittens.
You can't dance in puddles when it rains
or draw on steamy window panes,
and they won't let you create
scary monsters out of clay.

So if I were you,
I'd do the lot today!
Before
you're all grown up.